CGP has Year 1 Phonics sounded out!

CGP's Targeted Practice Books are packed with fun and friendly activities to build Year 1 pupils' confidence as they learn to read and write.

What's more, they follow the National Curriculum 'Letters and Sounds' programme, so you can be sure they cover everything children need to learn.

This is **Year 1 Targeted Practice Book 1**. It covers the early part of **Phase 5** of the 'Letters and Sounds' programme, including:

- The sounds **ay**, **oy**, **ea**, **ew**, **ou**, **au**, **ph**, **o-e**, **u-e**, **a-e**, **e-e**
- Reading and writing **tricky words**

What CGP is all about

Our sole aim here at CGP is to produce the highest quality books — carefully written, immaculately presented and dangerously close to being funny.

Then we work our socks off to get them out to you — at the cheapest possible prices.

How to Use this Book

In this Book

You'll meet...

 Word Birds: they'll help you read and write words and sentences

 Chatty Bats: they'll tell your helper what words to say in writing activities

 Jolly Jugglers: they'll help you practise those tricky words

Hints for Helpers

Here are a few things to bear in mind when using this book:

- CGP's Phonics series aligns with **Letters and Sounds**, the Department for Education's systematic synthetic phonics programme. Reception books 1-5 cover Phases 1, 2, 3 and 4. This Year 1 book focuses on the early part of Phase 5.

- The book should be worked through **in order**, as new content builds on content covered earlier in the book.

- In the introductory sections of the pages, a **grey line** under two or more letters in a word is a reminder that these letters work together to make **one sound**. '**Split digraphs**' (a pair of letters that work together, with another letter tucked in between them) are shown joined by a **loop**. ⟶ | cube |

- '**Tricky words**' are words with letters that have a sound that does not correspond to the expected sound, or that have a sound that has not yet been learned. These words need to be practised until they can be read straight away without blending sounds.

- '**Word frames**' are used in spelling and writing activities. Word frames for words that can be sounded out have boxes. There is **one box for each sound**.

- This resource requires children to match images to words. You may need to help children to **identify** some images they're not sure of.

Above all, promote a **positive, confident attitude** towards reading and writing by giving lots of praise and encouragement.

Contents

Written by Karen Bryant-Mole

Editors: Christopher Lindle, Sam Mann, Sam Norman
Reviewers: Ross Knaggs, Steph Lake, Clare Leck
With thanks to Holly Robinson and Lucy Towle for the proofreading.
ISBN: 978 1 78908 016 2

Images throughout the book from www.edu-clips.com
Printed by Elanders Ltd, Newcastle upon Tyne.
Based on the classic CGP style created by Richard Parsons.

Get Ready for Year 1 Phonics

Look at each card in turn. **Say** the sound.
Put a **tick** (✓) below each sound you can say.

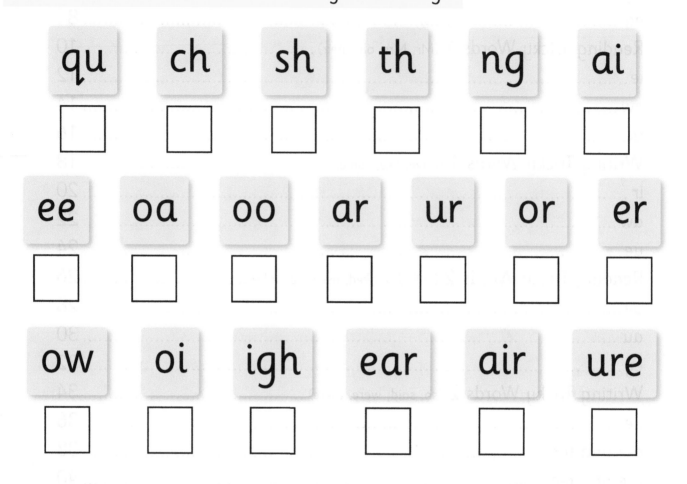

qu	ch	sh	th	ng	ai
☐	☐	☐	☐	☐	☐

ee	oa	oo	ar	ur	or	er
☐	☐	☐	☐	☐	☐	☐

ow	oi	igh	ear	air	ure
☐	☐	☐	☐	☐	☐

Read the captions under each picture.
Circle the correct caption.

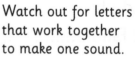

Watch out for letters that work together to make one sound.

jug

food

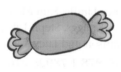

milk

sweet

crab

paint

Do you know the tricky words on the blocks?
If you can **read** the word, **circle** it.

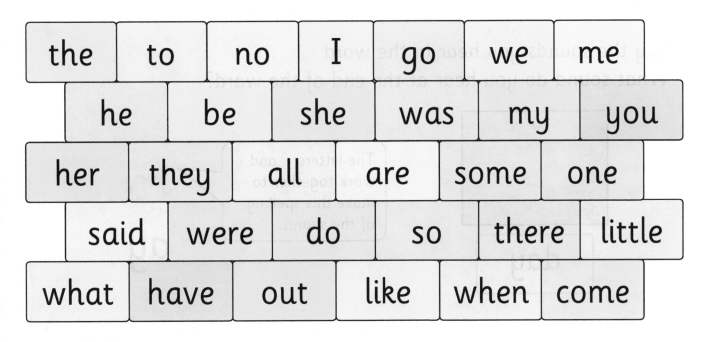

Listen to the tricky words these bats are saying.
Write each word in one of the special word frames.

I'm ready for Year 1 Phonics!

Phonics — Year 1 Book 1

ay

Say the sounds you hear in the word **day**.
What sound do you hear at the end of the word?

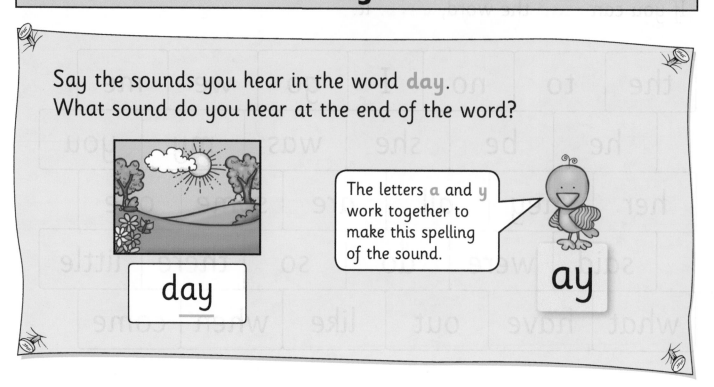

day

The letters **a** and **y** work together to make this spelling of the sound.

ay

Say the sounds in the word **tray**.
Draw a line under the letters that work together to make one sound.

tray

You often see this spelling of the sound when it's at the end of a word.

Read each caption. **Match** it to the correct picture.

crayon

spray

Find the card for the sound you hear at the end of the word **pay**.
Copy the letters into the word frame to complete the word.

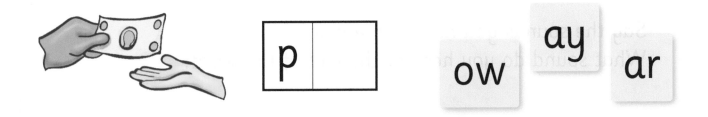

p	

ow   ay   ar

Say the words **hay** and **play**. **Say** the sounds in each word.
Write the letters in the word frames.

Word frames have one box for each sound.

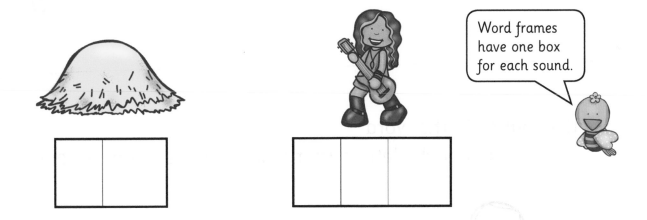

Read the sentence. **Circle** the best picture for the sentence.

Fay and Jay go away on holiday.

I know that the letters 'a' and 'y' work together to make the sound I hear at the end of the word 'day'.

oy

Say the sounds you hear in the word **boy**.
What sound do you hear at the end of the word?

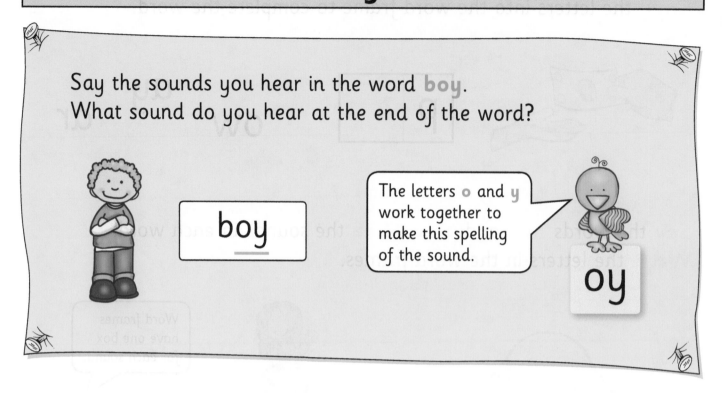

boy

The letters **o** and **y** work together to make this spelling of the sound.

oy

Say the sounds in the word **joy**.
Draw a line under the letters that work together to make one sound.

joy

The word **joy** is another word for **happiness**.

Read each caption. Match it to the correct picture.

destroy

oyster

Find the card for the sound you hear at the end of the word **annoy**. **Copy** the letters into the word frame to complete the word.

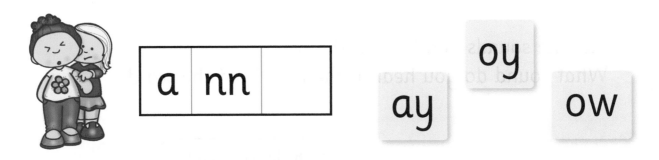

| a | nn | |

oy

ay

ow

Say the words **toy** and **enjoy**. **Say** the sounds in each word. **Write** the letters in the word frames.

If a sound has two letters, write them both in the same box.

Read the sentence. **Circle** the best picture for the sentence.

| Troy and Elroy dress up as cowboys. |

I know that the letters 'o' and 'y' work together to make the sound I hear at the end of the word 'boy'.

Phonics — Year 1 Book 1

ea

Say the sounds you hear in the word seal.
What sound do you hear in the middle of the word?

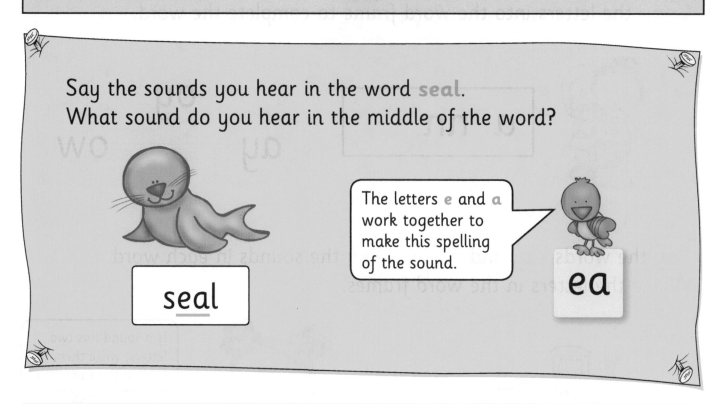

The letters e and a work together to make this spelling of the sound.

seal

ea

Say the sounds in the word beak.
Draw a line under the letters that work together to make one sound.

beak

Wow! That's a large beak!

Read each caption. Match it to the correct picture.

steal

peach

Find the card for the sound you hear in the middle of the word leaf.
Copy the letters into the word frame to complete the word.

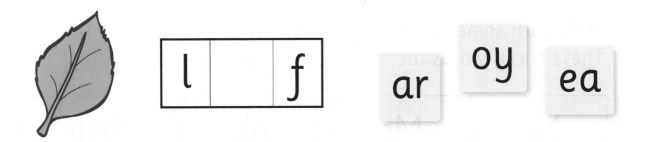

l		f

ar   oy   ea

Say the words bead and bean. Say the sounds in each word.
Write the letters in the word frames.

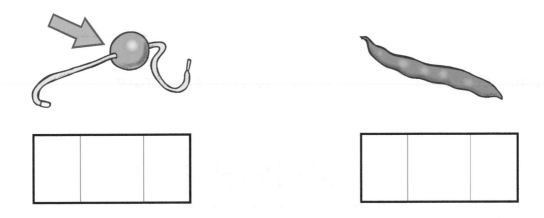

Read the sentence. Circle the best picture for the sentence.

Dean and Jean eat a meal.

I know that the letters 'e' and 'a' work together to make
the sound I hear in the middle of the word 'seal'.

Phonics — Year 1 Book 1

Reading Tricky Words 1

Let's learn some new tricky words.
These tricky words are **Mr**, **Mrs**, **oh** and **their**.

| Mr | Mrs | <u>oh</u> | <u>th</u>eir |

Did you know that **Mr** is a short way of writing the word **mister**.
Mrs is a short way of writing, and saying, the word **mistress**.

Read each caption. **Match** it to the correct picture.

Mr Patel

Mrs Patel

Look at the picture. **Read** the captions.
Circle the best caption for the picture.

Instead of a full stop, there's a special mark called an **exclamation mark**.

The exclamation mark tells you to read the words with feeling and emotion.

Oh!

Ow!

Read the sentences. Match each sentence to the correct picture.

They play with their toys.	

They read their books.	

Their teacher is cool.	

Read the sentence. Circle the best picture for the sentence.

Oh dear! Mr and Mrs Smith have forgotten their umbrella.

I can read the tricky words 'Mr', 'Mrs', 'oh' and 'their'.
I know what an exclamation mark is.

ie

Say the sounds you hear in the word tie.
What sound do you hear at the end of the word?

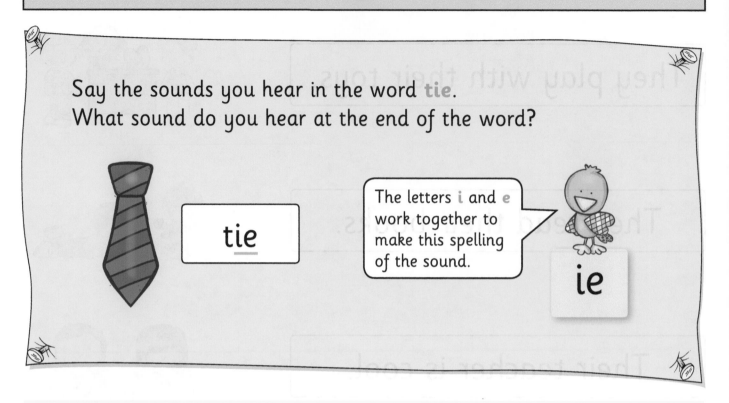

tie

The letters i and e work together to make this spelling of the sound.

ie

Say the sounds in the word spies.
Draw a line under the letters that work together to make one sound.

spies

You'll never see this spelling of the sound at the start of a word.

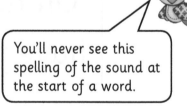

Read each caption. Match it to the correct picture.

flies

fried

Find the card for the sound you hear at the end of the word lie.
Copy the letters into the word frame to complete the word.

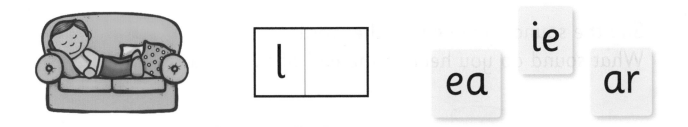

l

ie

ea   ar

Say the words cries and dries. Say the sounds in each word.
Write the letters in the word frames.

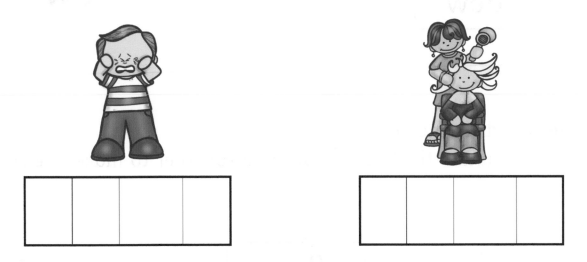

Read the sentence. Circle the best picture for the sentence.

I tried the pie and fries.

I know that the letters 'i' and 'e' work together to make
the sound I hear at the end of the word 'tie'.

Phonics — Year 1 Book 1

ew

Say the sounds you hear in the word dew.
What sound do you hear at the end of the word?

dew

The letters e and w
work together to
make this spelling
of the sound.

ew

Say the sounds in the word flew.
Draw a line under the letters that work together to make one sound.

flew

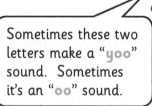

Sometimes these two
letters make a "yoo"
sound. Sometimes
it's an "oo" sound.

Read each caption. Match it to the correct picture.

jewel

screw

Find the card for the sound you hear in the middle of the word **newt**. Copy the letters into the word frame to complete the word.

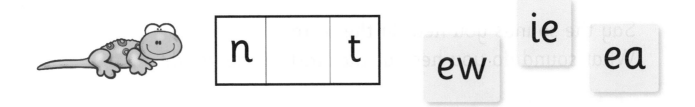

n		t

ew   **ie**   **ea**

Say the words **stew** and **grew**. Say the sounds in each word. Write the letters in the word frames.

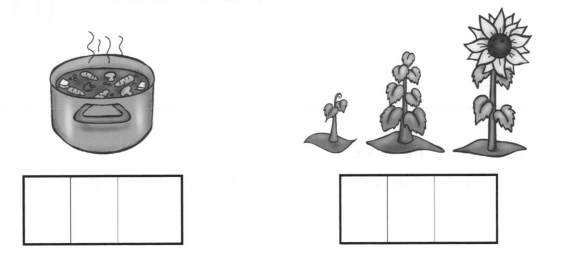

Read the sentence. Circle the best picture for the sentence.

Lewis and Drew are the news crew.

I know that the letters 'e' and 'w' work together to make the sound I hear at the end of the word 'dew'.

ou

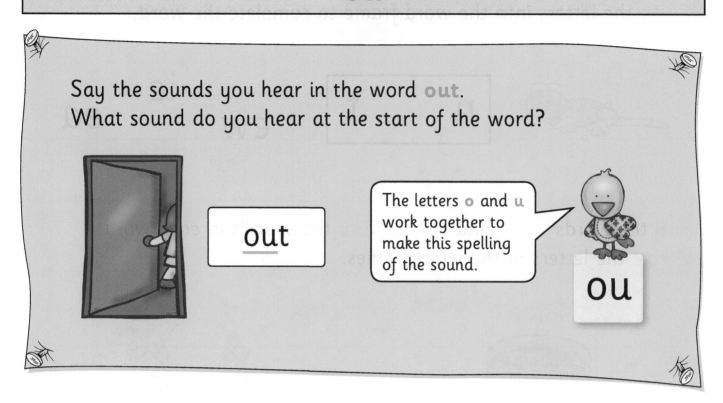

Say the sounds you hear in the word out.
What sound do you hear at the start of the word?

out

The letters o and u work together to make this spelling of the sound.

ou

Say the sounds in the word trout.
Draw a line under the letters that work together to make one sound.

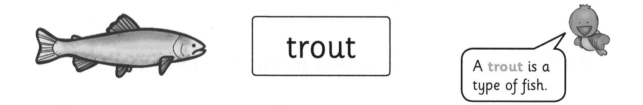

trout

A trout is a type of fish.

Read each caption. Match it to the correct picture.

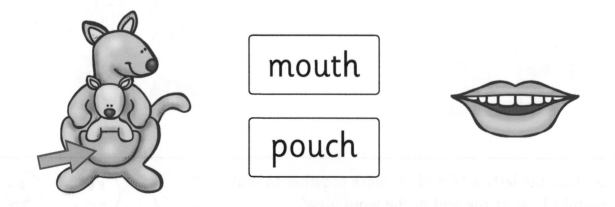

mouth

pouch

Find the card for the sound you hear in the middle of the word **shout**.
Copy the letters into the word frame to complete the word.

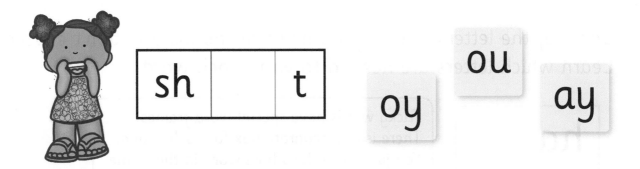

Say the words **loud** and **round**. **Say** the sounds in each word.
Write the letters in the word frames.

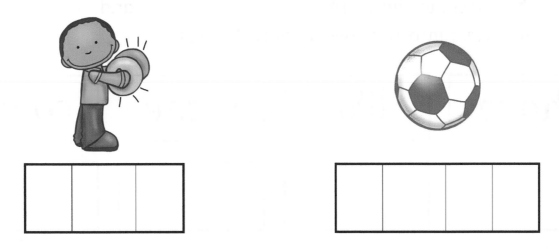

Read the sentence. **Circle** the best picture for the sentence.

Hound is another word for dog.

I know that the letters 'o' and 'u' work together to make the sound I hear at the beginning of the word 'out'.

Phonics — Year 1 Book 1

Writing Tricky Words 1

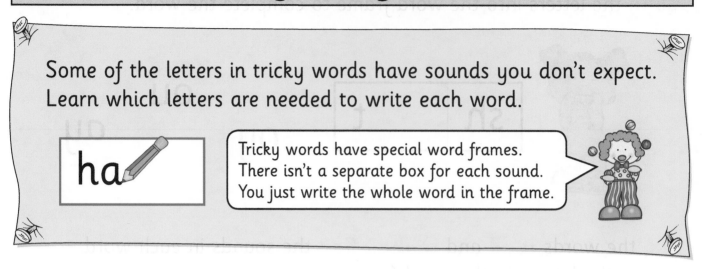

Some of the letters in tricky words have sounds you don't expect.
Learn which letters are needed to write each word.

ha

> Tricky words have special word frames.
> There isn't a separate box for each sound.
> You just write the whole word in the frame.

Name the letters in the words **have**, **like**, **some** and **come**.
Copy the letters into the special word frames.

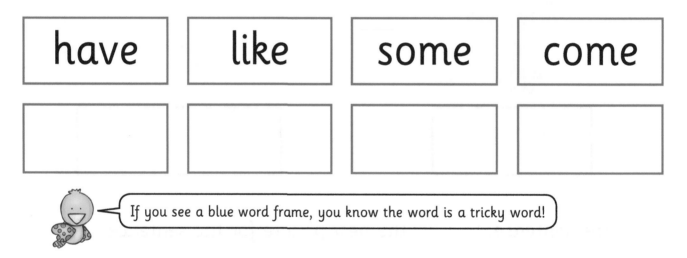

| have | like | some | come |

> If you see a blue word frame, you know the word is a tricky word!

Do you see the bat? **Listen** to the sentence it's saying.
Write the sentence in the word frames.

I have a cat.

> One of these tricky words is a word you have learned to write before.

> Don't forget the full stop at the end.

Here are some more bats. **Listen** to the sentence each bat is saying, then **write** it in the word frames.

We like bugs.

You need a capital letter at the start of the first word.

Dad has some fish.

Watch out for the tricky word.

Come and get it.

Practise these tricky words until you can write them straight away.

I can write sentences that include the tricky words 'have', 'like', 'some' and 'come'.

ir

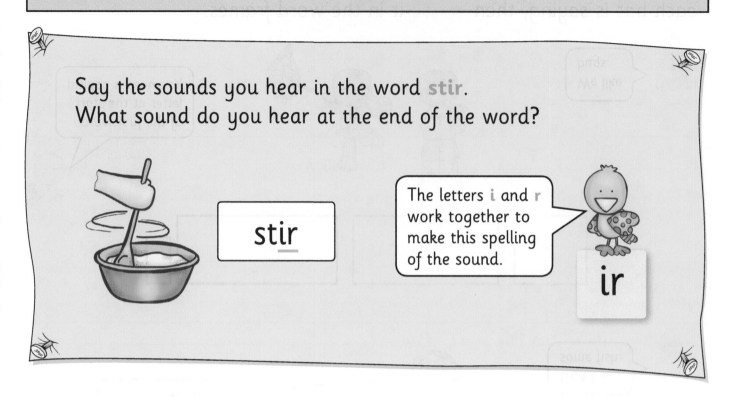

Say the sounds you hear in the word stir.
What sound do you hear at the end of the word?

stir

The letters i and r work together to make this spelling of the sound.

ir

Say the sounds in the word fir.
Draw a line under the letters that work together to make one sound.

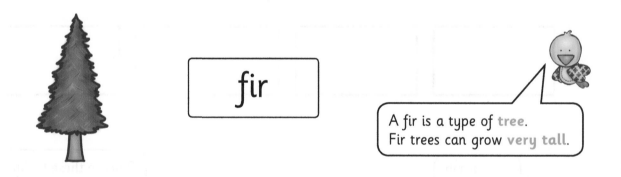

fir

A fir is a type of tree.
Fir trees can grow very tall.

Read each caption. Match it to the correct picture.

skirt

squirt

Find the card for the sound you hear in the middle of the word shirt.
Copy the letters into the word frame to complete the word.

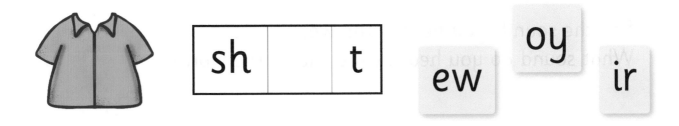

Say the words dirt and bird. Say the sounds in each word.
Write the letters in the word frames.

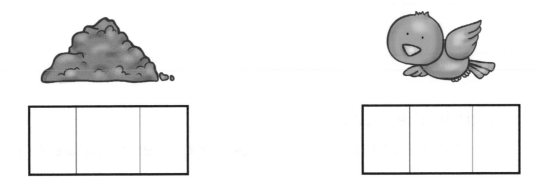

Read the sentence. Circle the best picture for the sentence.

Kirstin is the first girl to twirl.

I know that the letters 'i' and 'r' work together
to make the sound I hear at the end of the word 'stir'.

Phonics — Year 1 Book 1

aw

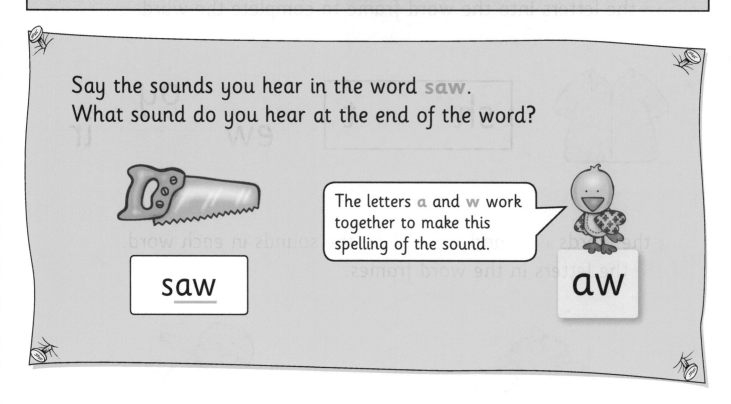

Say the sounds you hear in the word saw.
What sound do you hear at the end of the word?

saw

The letters a and w work together to make this spelling of the sound.

aw

Say the sounds in the word hawk.
Draw a line under the letters that work together to make one sound.

hawk

A hawk is a type of bird.

Read each caption. Match it to the correct picture.

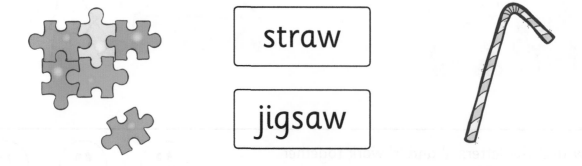

straw

jigsaw

Find the card for the sound you hear at the end of the word **paw**.
Copy the letters into the word frame to complete the word.

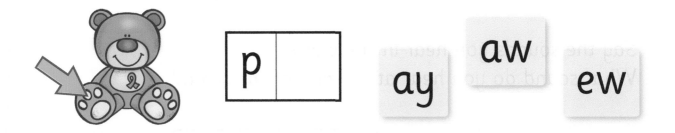

p	

ay   aw   ew

Say the words **dawn** and **claw**. **Say** the sounds in each word.
Write the letters in the word frames.

Read the sentence. **Circle** the best picture for the sentence.

Miss Shaw saw a fawn on the lawn.

I know that the letters 'a' and 'w' work together
to make the sound I hear at the end of the word 'saw'.

Phonics — Year 1 Book 1

ue

Say the sounds you hear in the word blue
What sound do you hear at the end of the word?

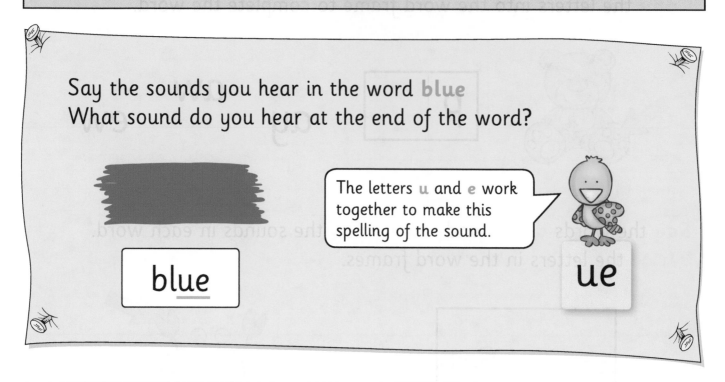

blue

The letters u and e work together to make this spelling of the sound.

ue

Say the sounds in the word cue.
Draw a line under the letters that work together to make one sound.

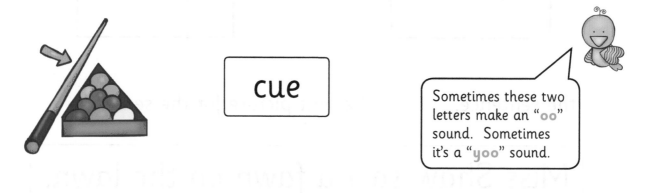

cue

Sometimes these two letters make an "oo" sound. Sometimes it's a "yoo" sound.

Read each caption. Match it to the correct picture.

avenue

statue

Find the card for the sound you hear at the end of the word glue.
Copy the letters into the word frame to complete the word.

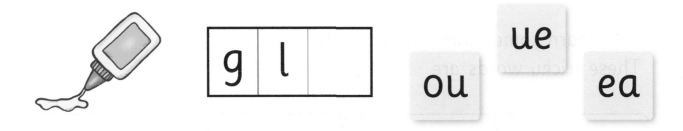

g l

ue

ou

ea

Say the words clue and true. Say the sounds in each word.
Write the letters in the word frames.

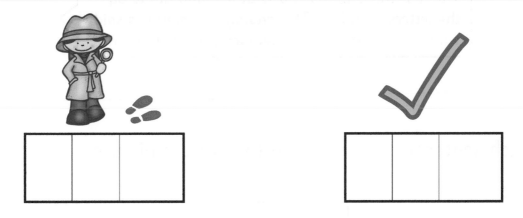

Read the sentence. Circle the best picture for the sentence.

Sue is going to rescue Prue.

I know that the letters 'u' and 'e' work together
to make the sound I hear at the end of the word 'blue'.

Reading Tricky Words 2

Let's learn some more tricky words.
These tricky words are called, looked, asked and people.

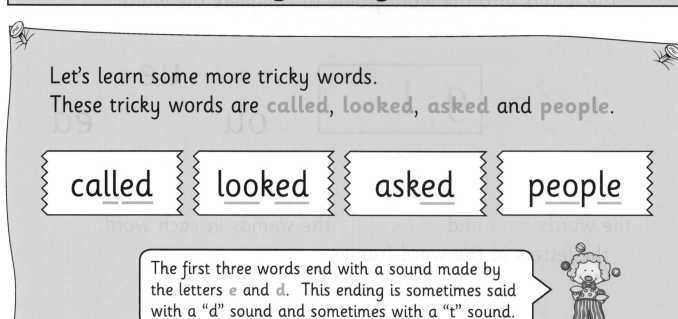

| called | looked | asked | people |

The first three words end with a sound made by the letters **e** and **d**. This ending is sometimes said with a "d" sound and sometimes with a "t" sound.

Read each sentence. **Match** it to the correct picture.

I looked.

I called.

Look at the picture. **Read** the captions.
Circle the correct caption for the picture.

three people

six people

Read the sentences. Match each sentence to the correct picture.

They looked at the clouds.

She had asked for some tea.

The new boy is called Kirk.

Read the sentences. Circle the best picture for the sentences.

The people on the boat called and asked for help. They looked upset.

oe

Say the sounds you hear in the word toes.
What sound do you hear in the middle of the word?

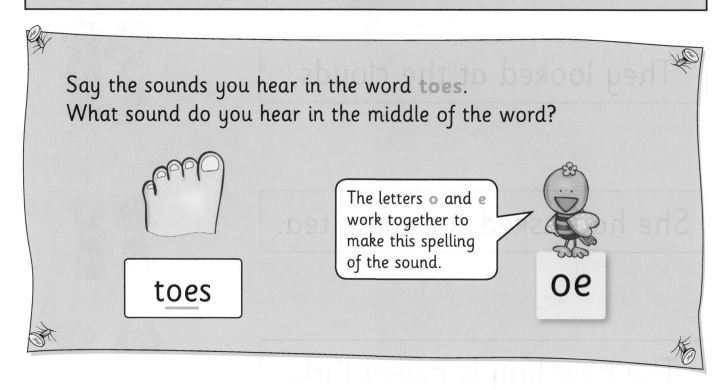

toes

The letters o and e work together to make this spelling of the sound.

oe

Say the sounds in the word foe.
Draw a line under the letters that work together to make one sound.

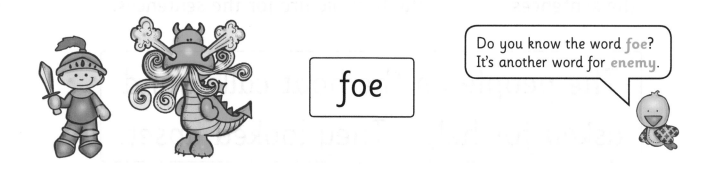

foe

Do you know the word foe? It's another word for enemy.

Read each caption. Match it to the correct picture.

dominoes

buffaloes

Find the card for the sound you hear at the end of the word **hoe**.
Copy the letters into the word frame to complete the word.

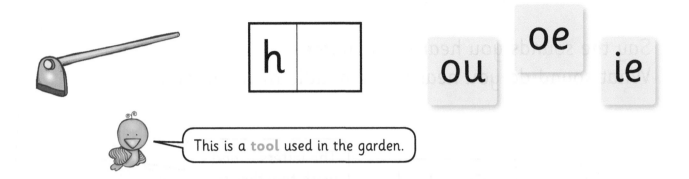

h | |

oe

ou   ie

This is a **tool** used in the garden.

Say the words **woe** and **doe**. **Say** the sounds in each word.
Write the letters in the word frames.

Woe is another word for **sadness**. A **doe** is a **female deer**.

Read the sentence. **Circle** the best picture for the sentence.

Roscoe goes on tiptoe.

I know that the letters 'o' and 'e' work together to
make the sound I hear in the middle of the word 'toes'.

Phonics — Year 1 Book 1

au

Say the sounds you hear in the name Paul.
What sound do you hear in the middle of the name?

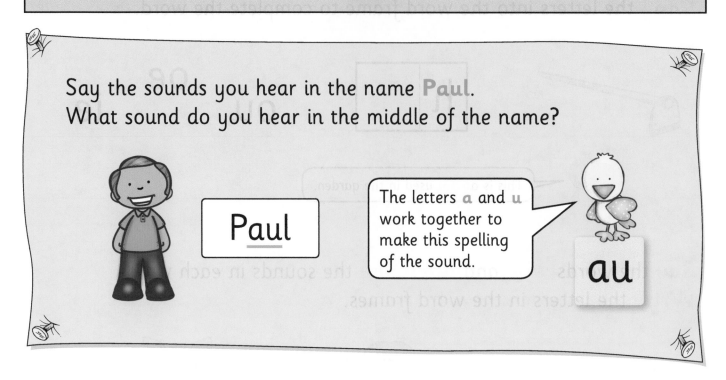

Paul

The letters a and u work together to make this spelling of the sound.

au

Say the sounds in the word gaunt.
Draw a line under the letters that work together to make one sound.

gaunt

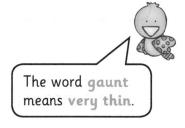

The word gaunt means very thin.

Read each caption. Match it to the correct picture.

applaud

launch

Find the card for the sound you hear in the middle of the word taut. Copy the letters into the word frame to complete the word.

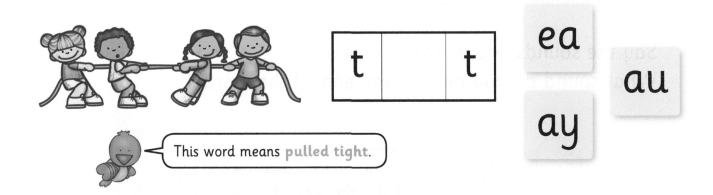

| t | | t |

This word means pulled tight.

Say the words haul and haunt. Say the sounds in each word. Write the letters in the word frames.

The word haul means to pull.

| | | |

| | | |

Read the sentence. Circle the best picture for the sentence.

Shaun and Maud applaud the astronaut.

I know that the letters 'a' and 'u' work together to make the sound I hear in the middle of the name 'Paul'.

ey

Say the sounds you hear in the word key.
What sound do you hear at the end of the word?

key

The letters e and y work together to make this spelling of the sound.

ey

Say the sounds in the word medley.
Draw a line under the letters that work together to make one sound.

medley

The word medley means a mix or assortment.

Read each caption. Match it to the correct picture.

trolley

hockey

Find the card for the sound you hear at the end of the word valley.
Copy the letters into the word frame to complete the word.

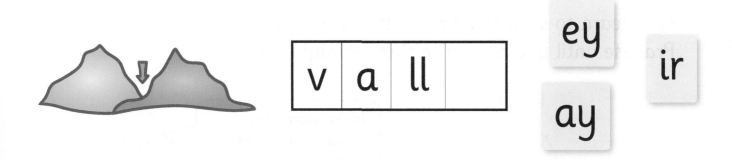

v	a	ll	

ey

ay

ir

Say the words donkey and chimney. Say the sounds in each word. Write the letters in the word frames.

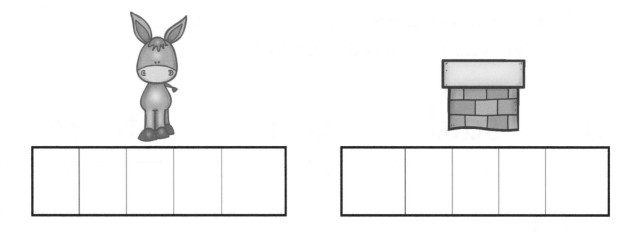

Read the sentence. Circle the best picture for the sentence.

Kelsey and Stanley are jockeys.

I know that the letters 'e' and 'y' work together
to make the sound I hear at the end of the word 'key'.

Writing Tricky Words 2

Let's learn to spell some more tricky words.
Practise until you can write them straight away.

Tricky words are useful words to know. You'll use them a lot.

Name the letters in the words **so**, **said**, **were** and **there**.
Copy the letters into the special word frames.

so	said	were	there

Listen carefully to the sentence the bat is saying.
Write the sentence in the word frames.

It was so hot.

There's one tricky word here that you have learned to write before.

Here are three more bats. **Listen** to the sentence each bat is saying, then **write** it in the word frames.

We were in the pool.

There are three tricky words this time.

She said not to run.

And three tricky words here, too.

We had fun there.

Don't forget the capital letter and the full stop.

I can write sentences that include the tricky words 'so', 'said', 'were' and 'there'.

Phonics — Year 1 Book 1

i-e

Say the sounds you hear in the word **line**.
Say the sound you hear in the middle of the word.

The letters **i** and **e** work together to make this spelling of the sound.

There's a loop joining the two letters. It shows that they work together even though they aren't written next to each other.

line

i e

Say the sounds in the word **time**. **Draw a loop** to join the letters that work together to make one sound.

time

I like to think of this as the word **tie** with the letter for the last sound, "**m**", tucked in between the **i** and the **e**.

Read each caption. **Match** it to the correct picture.

kite

prize

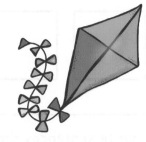

Find the cards for the sound in the middle of the word pipe.
Copy the letters into the word frame to complete the word.

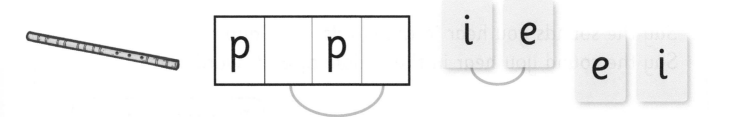

p		p	

i e

e i

Say the words ride and hive. Say the sounds in each word.
Write the letters in the word frames.

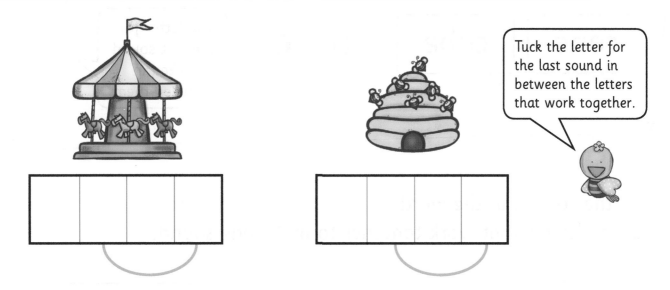

Tuck the letter for the last sound in between the letters that work together.

Read the sentence. Circle the best picture for the sentence.

Clive has a bike but Mike likes to drive.

o-e and u-e

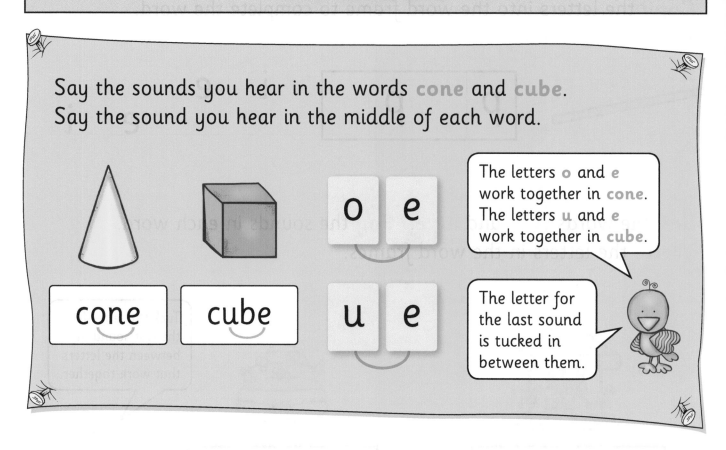

Say the sounds you hear in the words cone and cube.
Say the sound you hear in the middle of each word.

The letters o and e work together in cone. The letters u and e work together in cube.

The letter for the last sound is tucked in between them.

cone   cube

o   e

u   e

Say the sounds in the word rude. Draw a loop to join the letters that work together to make one sound.

rude

Hey! The letters u and e are another pair of letters that sometimes have a "yoo" sound and sometimes an "oo" sound.

Read each caption. Match it to the correct picture.

tube

bone

Find the cards for the sound you hear in the middle of the word rope.
Copy the letters into the word frame to complete the word.

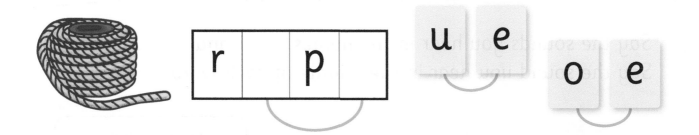

Say the words mule and hole. Say the sounds in each word.
Write the letters in the word frames.

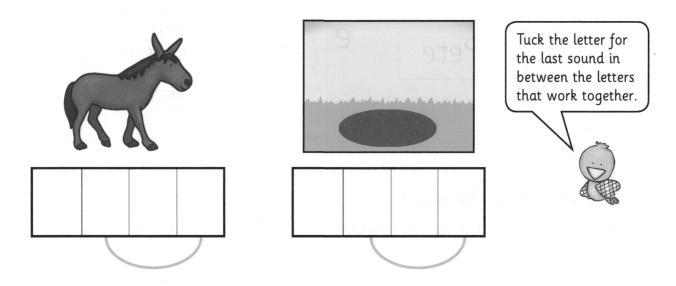

Tuck the letter for the last sound in between the letters that work together.

Read the sentence. Circle the best picture for the sentence.

Simone plays a tune on the flute.

I know that the letters 'o' and 'e', and 'u' and 'e', can work together even when they aren't written next to each other.

Phonics — Year 1 Book 1

a-e and e-e

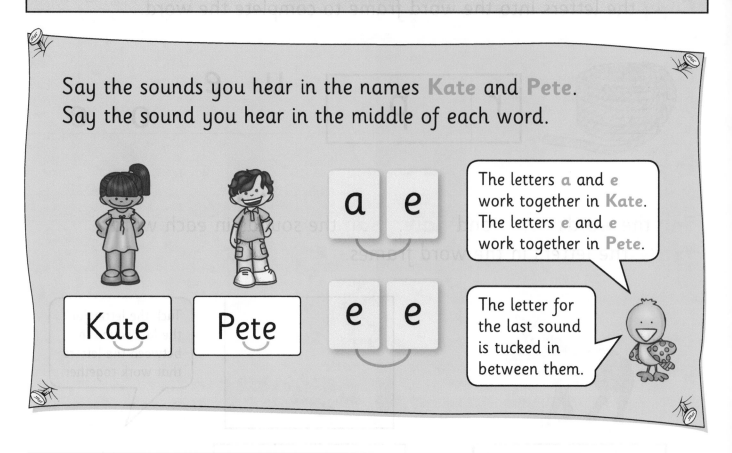

Say the sounds you hear in the names Kate and Pete.
Say the sound you hear in the middle of each word.

a e

Kate   Pete

e e

The letters a and e work together in Kate. The letters e and e work together in Pete.

The letter for the last sound is tucked in between them.

Say the sounds in the word compete. Draw a loop to join the letters that work together to make one sound.

compete

You compete in a competition!

Read each caption. Match it to the correct picture.

plane

athlete

Find the cards for the sound you hear in the middle of the word **cake**. **Copy** the letters into the word frame to complete the word.

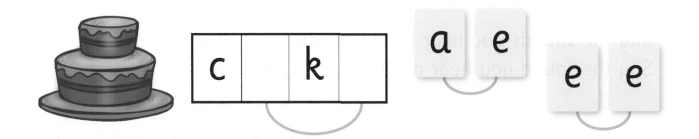

Say the words **gate** and **swede**. **Say** the sounds in each word. **Write** the letters in the word frames.

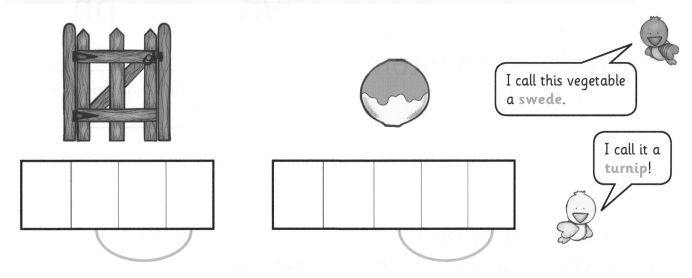

I call this vegetable a **swede**.

I call it a **turnip**!

Read the sentence. **Circle** the best picture for the sentence.

Jade will amaze you on the trapeze.

I know that the letters 'a' and 'e', and 'e' and 'e', can work together even when they aren't written next to each other.

wh and ph

Say the sounds you hear in the words whisk and phantom. Say the sound you hear at the start of each word.

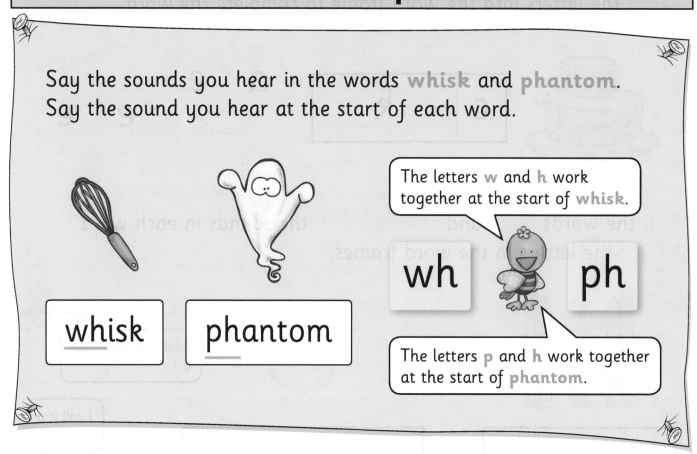

The letters w and h work together at the start of whisk.

wh

ph

whisk

phantom

The letters p and h work together at the start of phantom.

Say the sounds in the word whelk. Draw a line under the two letters that work together to make one sound.

whelk

A whelk is a type of snail that lives in the sea.

Say the sounds in the word dolphin. Draw a line under the two letters that work together to make one sound.

dolphin

Dolphins live in the sea, too!

Read each caption. Match it to the correct picture.

wheel

alphabet

Say the sound you hear at the start of phone and the sound you hear at the start of wheat. Find the correct card for each sound. Copy the letters into the word frames to complete the words.

	o	n	e

	ea	t

wh   ph

Read the sentence. Circle the best picture for the sentence.

Whitney gave her nephew an elephant.

I know that 'w' and 'h', and 'p' and 'h', work together to make the sounds at the start of 'whisk' and 'phantom'.

Phonics — Year 1 Book 1

Grand Finale

Read each word. Find them hidden among the letters
on the caterpillar. Circle them.

lake	yawn	blue	girl

Look at the picture. Read each caption.
If you see that object in the picture, circle the caption.

seesaw	flagpole	slide

roundabout	bookcase

Read the captions in the speech bubbles.
Match each caption to the child you think is saying it.

Ouch! Hooray! Humph!

Do you like playing games?
Match the name of each game to the correct picture.

pin the tail on the donkey

dominoes

hide and seek

snakes and ladders

Phonics — Year 1 Book 1

Read the sentences. Circle the animal they are describing.

What am I?

I am black and white.

I have wings and a beak.

I enjoy swimming.

Let's finish with a joke!
Read the question. Can you guess the answer?
Turn your workbook upside down. Read the answer.

What has wheels and flies?

A rubbish truck!

I've had fun practising what I've learned.

E1OW111